MOSAICS

Clarinet

Book 1

65 solo pieces
by James Rae

Introduction

This collection of graded pieces for the clarinet was written in order to develop the many technical, musical and interpretive skills required by performers so that they become conversant with a wide variety of styles. These pieces draw on my experiences as a composer, performer and teacher, to present a range of dynamic and engaging pieces. The book is organised in order of difficulty so the player can easily map his or her progress. The pieces in Book 1 are from beginner to approximately Grade 5 standard, and those in Book 2 are approximately Grade 6 to Grade 8 standard.

Many of the pieces could effectively be presented in programmes for music festivals and the more advanced pieces are be suitable for inclusion in the solo performance sections of GCSE, A Level and International Baccalaureate music exams.

As a general rule when playing these pieces it is best to note that:

▶ accidentals apply only to their octave
▶ the swing element in jazz is triplet-like at slow tempos, but lessens and becomes straighter as the tempo increases.

I hope that you enjoy playing these pieces.

James Rae

Published by
Trinity College London
www.trinitycollege.com

Registered in the UK
Company no. 02683033
Charity no. 1014792

Printed in England by Halstan, Amersham, Bucks.

Contents

1. On Parade

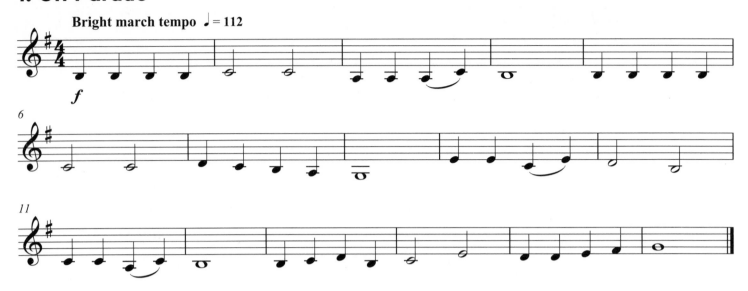

2. A Sad Day

3. Chocolate Novelty

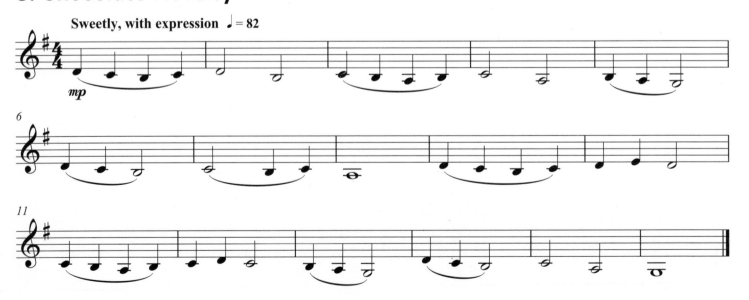

4. Cossack Dance

5. Off to the Match!

6. Tea and Bun

7. Green Pastures

8. Wigwam Rock

9. Space March

10. A Gentle Stroll

11. May the Fourths be With You

12. Cool Dance

13. March of the Processed Peas

14. Going down with Eees

15. Da Capo Waltz

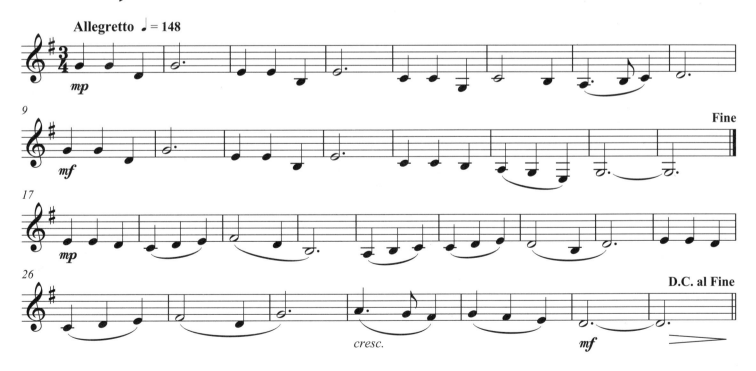

16. Blues in the Dark

17. Bring your own Camel!

18. Tyrolean Banquet

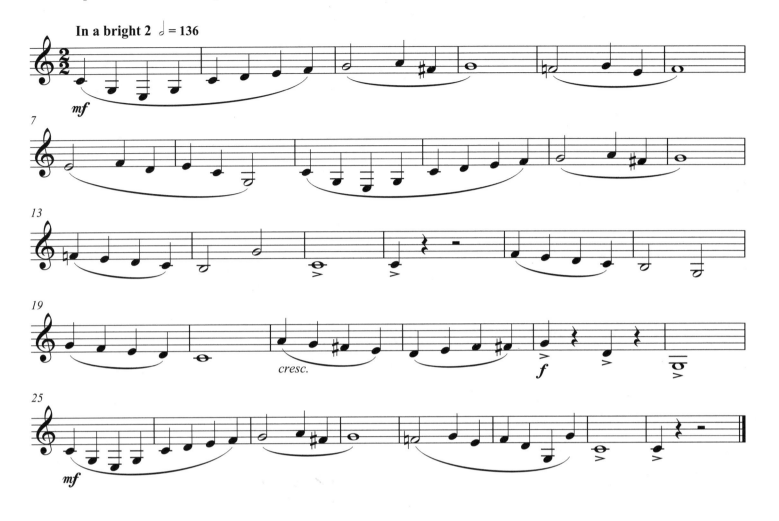

19. Waltz for a Tsar

20. Zig-Zag

21. County Jig

22. Beyond the Mist

23. Surbiton Rock

24. Sidewalk Shuffle

25. Rise and Fall

Watch for the jumps. 10/5/17.

SLURS.

14

26. Long Shadows

27. Shiver me Timbers!

L = long!
S = short!

10/5/17.

15

28. Meerkat Mazurka

29. Self-employment Blues

16

30. Scherzo

31. Silk Street Swing

32. Schnitzel Waltz

33. Cop This!

18

34. Andante in A

35. Invaders March

19

36. Drifting

37. Basil the Bionic Flea

38. Neeps 'n' Tatties

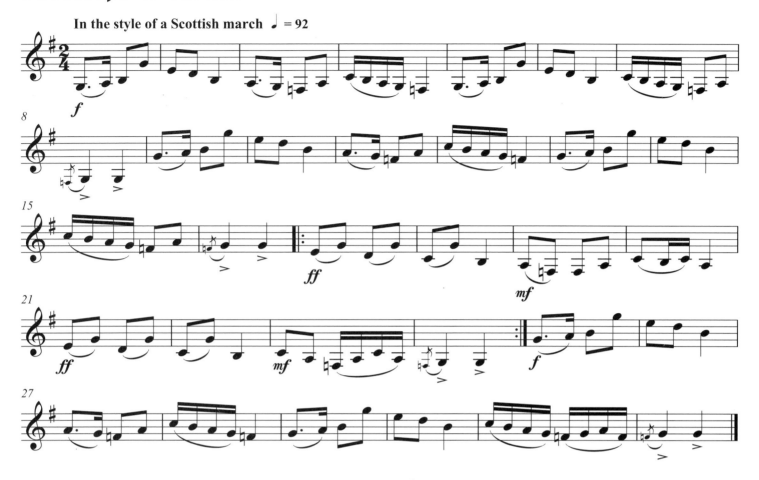

39. Black Pepper?

40. Coconut Rumba

41. Imperial Waltz

42. Schedule D

43. The Demon's Delight

44. Nine over the Eight

45. Captain Funk

46. Chelsea Blues

47. The Seventh Dimension

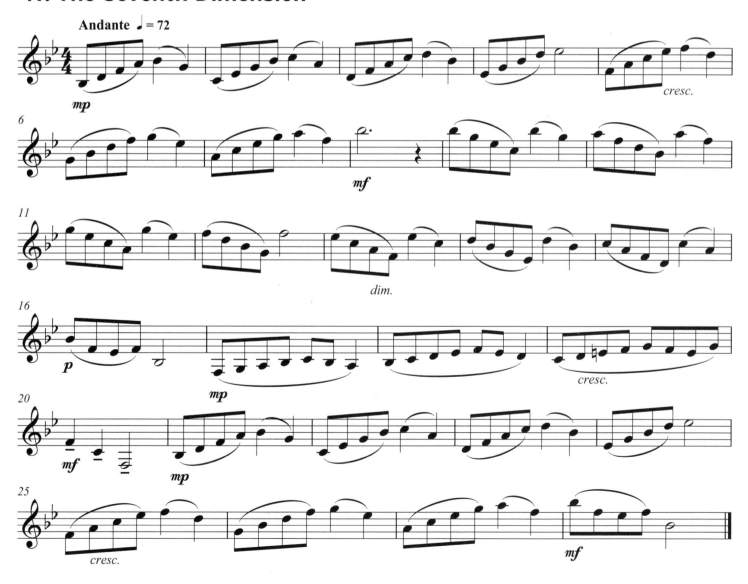

48. Dot to Dot

28

49. A Major Development

50. Slap-up Supper

Slow aggressive Rock feel ♩ = 84

51. Paddy's Rant

Lively jig tempo ♩ = 148

52. Full of Beans

Bright swing tempo ♩ = 148

53. Rum Truffle Waltz

54. Five Past Five

55. Regimental March

56. Arabesque

57. Conundrum

58. On the Rocks

59. Rockin' Roland

60. The Unexpected

61. Fake Five

62. Etude in C

63. Odd Bods

64. Pile Driver

65. Shifting Winds